# ●Fun with Eng

# Modern Quotations

**George Beal**
**Illustrated by Peter Stevenson**

ALL ANIMALS ARE EQUAL.
BUT SOME ANIMALS ARE
MORE EQUAL THAN OTHERS.

KING*f*ISHER

General editor: John Grisewood
Editor: Nicola Barber
Illustrations: Peter Stevenson
             (Kathy Jakeman Illustration)
Design: Robert Wheeler Associates


KINGFISHER
Kingfisher Publications Plc
New Penderel House, 283–288 High Holborn,
London WC1V 7HZ

This edition published by Kingfisher Publications Plc 2000
10 9 8 7 6 5 4 3 2 1
1(TR)/0100/EDK/(MA)/135EDI

A CIP catalogue record for this book is available from
the British Library

ISBN 0 7534 0462 1

Printed in Spain

Everyone uses quotations in their everyday speech, sometimes without realizing that they are, in fact, quoting the words of someone else. Probably the most-quoted of all people is William Shakespeare. There exist several large volumes which are entirely devoted to quotations from his works. This book concentrates on modern quotations, mostly first used in the present century. A key-word system is used to find a particular quotation – for example, if you want to look up who wrote 'O to be in England, now that April's there', you look up **England** and find that the quotation was originated by Robert Browning. If you want to know more about the person quoted you can turn to the alphabetical list at the end of the book. The quotations in boxes are, in fact, misquotations.

**abnormal**
If it weren't for the fact that all of us are slightly abnormal, there wouldn't be any point in giving each person a separate name.

UGO BETTI.

**abstract**
Abstract art? A product of the untalented, sold by the unprincipled to the utterly bewildered.

AL CAPP.

**acting**
Acting is not a profession for adults.

LAURENCE OLIVIER.

The general consensus seems to be that I don't act at all.

GARY COOPER.

The hardest kind of acting works only if you look as if you are not acting at all.

HENRY FONDA.

**actors**
Seventy-five per cent of being successful as an actor is pure luck. The rest is just endurance.

GENE HACKMAN.

Actors and burglars work better at night.

SIR CEDRIC HARDWICKE.

**adapting**
Human creatures have a marvellous power of adapting themselves to necessity.

GEORGE GISSING.

**adults**
Adults are obsolete children.

DR SEUSS.

**adventure**
Adventure is the result of poor planning.

COL. BLASHFORD-SNELL.

**advice**
No-one wants advice – only corroboration.

JOHN STEINBECK.

**alive**
It's a funny old world; a man's lucky if he gets out alive.

W.C. FIELDS.

**alone** I want to be alone. GRETA GARBO. Her true words were: "I like to be alone.".

**America**
America is God's Crucible, the Great Melting-Pot.

ISRAEL ZANGWILL.

**amused**
We are not amused.

QUEEN VICTORIA.

**angels**
Angels can fly because they take themselves lightly.

G.K. CHESTERTON.

**antique**
An antique is something that's been useless so long it's still in good condition.

FRANKLIN P. JONES.

**applaud**
If they liked you, they didn't applaud – they just let you live.

BOB HOPE.

**archaeologist**
An archaeologist is the best husband a woman can have; the older she gets the more interested he is in her.

AGATHA CHRISTIE.

**arguing**
I am not arguing with you – I am telling you.

JAMES MCNEILL WHISTLER.

**argument**
The best way I know to win an argument is to start by being in the right.

LORD HAILSHAM.

The only way to get the best of an argument is to avoid it.

DALE CARNEGIE.

**armour**
Armour is the kind of clothing worn by a man whose tailor was a blacksmith.

AMBROSE BIERCE.

**assassination**
Assassination is the extreme form of censorship.

GEORGE BERNARD SHAW.

**atheist**
I am an atheist still, thank God.

LUIS BUÑUEL.

The worst moment for an atheist is when he feels grateful and doesn't know who to thank.

WENDY WARD.

**audience**
If all the world's a stage, and all the men and women merely players, where do all the audiences come from?

DENIS NORDEN.

A work of art does not exist without its audience.

RICHARD HAMILTON.

The only real teacher of acting is the audience.

GEORGE C. SCOTT.

**average**
Most people are such fools that it really is no compliment to say that a man is above average.

W. SOMERSET MAUGHAM.

4

# B

**badly**
If a thing is worth doing it is worth doing badly.

G.K. CHESTERTON.

**ball**
The ball is man's most disastrous invention, not excluding the wheel.

ROBERT MORLEY.

**bank**
Banks lend you money as people lend you an umbrella when the sun is shining and want it back when it starts to rain.

SIR EDWARD BEDDINGTON-BEHRENS.

A bank is a place that will lend you money if you can prove that you don't need it.

BOB HOPE.

**bat**
Twinkle, twinkle little bat!
How I wonder what you're at!

LEWIS CARROLL.

**beard**
An irregular greying beard was a decoration to a face which badly needed assistance.

EDGAR WALLACE.

I grew a beard for Nero, in *Quo Vadis*, but Metro-Goldwyn-Mayer thought it didn't look real, so I had to wear a false one.

PETER USTINOV.

**beautiful**
Remember that the most beautiful things in the world are the most useless; peacocks and lilies for instance.

JOHN RUSKIN.

**Bible**
The number one book of the ages was written by a committee, and it was called the Bible.

LOUIS B. MAYER.

**bigger**
The bigger they come, the harder they fall.

ROBERT FITZSIMMONS.

**billiards**
Proficiency at billiards is proof of a misspent youth.

HERBERT SPENCER.

**blind**
In the country of the blind the one-eyed man is king.

H.G.WELLS. 5

DID YOU KNOW THAT AMBROSE BIERCE SAID THAT A BORE IS A FELLOW WHO TALKS WHEN YOU WANT HIM TO LISTEN.

## blushing

Man is the only animal that blushes – or needs to.

MARK TWAIN.

## boaster

A boaster is not always a liar.

ERIC PARTRIDGE.

## books

The only books I have in my library are books that other people have lent me.

ANATOLE FRANCE.

When I am dead, I hope it may be said: "His sins were scarlet, but his books were read."

HILAIRE BELLOC.

## bore

A fellow who talks when you wish him to listen.

AMBROSE BIERCE.

## box

We give people a box in the suburbs. It's called a house, and every night they sit in it staring at another box, in the morning they run off to another box called an office, and at the weekends they get into another box, on wheels this time, and grope their way through endless traffic jams.

CAROLINE KELLY.

## boxing

Boxing is glamorized violence.

LORD TAYLOR OF GRYFE.

## bravery

There is no such thing as bravery; only degrees of fear.

JOHN WAINWRIGHT.

## breakfast

If you want to eat well in England, eat three breakfasts.

W. SOMERSET MAUGHAM.

## brother

I want to be the white man's brother, not his brother-in-law.

MARTIN LUTHER KING.

## buck

The buck stops here.

HARRY S. TRUMAN (*Sign on President Truman's desk*)

## cards

When a man tells me he's going to put all his cards on the table, I always look up his sleeve.

LORD HORE-BELISHA.

## care

If I'd known how old I was going to be I'd have taken better care of myself.

ADOLPH ZUKOR.

## celebrity

A celebrity is a person who works hard all his life to become known, then wears dark glasses to avoid being recognized.

FRED ALLEN.

**cheese**
How can you govern a country which produces 246 different kinds of cheese?

CHARLES DE GAULLE.

**child**
When a child is grown up, it's time the parents learned to stand on their own feet.

FRANCIS.HOPE.

**cinema**
The cinema is not a slice of life. It's a piece of cake.

ALFRED HITCHCOCK.

Cinema is the most beautiful fraud in the world.

JEAN-LUC GODARD.

**city**
The city is not a concrete jungle, it is a human zoo.

DESMOND MORRIS.

**civil servants**
Some civil servants are neither servants nor civil.

WINSTON CHURCHILL.

**clever**
I know I'm not clever, but I'm always right.

J.M. BARRIE.

**club**
I don't want to belong to any club that will accept me as a member.

GROUCHO MARX.

**comeback**
I'm always making a comeback, but nobody ever tells me where I've been.

BILLIE HOLLIDAY.

**comedian**
A comedian does funny things; a good comedian does things funny.

BUSTER KEATON.

**comedy**
Comedy is simply a funny way of being serious.

PETER USTINOV.

All I need to make a comedy is a park, a policeman and a pretty girl.

CHARLIE CHAPLIN.

**comment**
Comment is free, but facts are sacred.

C.P. SCOTT.

**common man**
The century on which we are entering – the century which will come out of this war – can be and must be the century of the common man.

HENRY WALLACE.

**composers**
Composers should write tunes that chauffeurs and errand boys can whistle.

SIR THOMAS BEECHAM.

7

**computer**
To err is human, but to really foul things up requires a computer.
PAUL EHRLICH.

**conscience**
I cannot and I will not cut my conscience to fit this year's fashions.
LILLIAN HELLMAN.

**consequences**
You can do anything in this world if you are prepared to take the consequences.
W. SOMERSET MAUGHAM.

**contract**
A verbal contract isn't worth the paper it's written on.
SAM GOLDWYN.

**cook**
The cook was a good cook, as cooks go; and as cooks go, she went.
'SAKI' (H.H. MUNRO).

**courtesy**
Courtesy is not dead. It has merely taken refuge in Great Britain.
GEORGES DUHAMEL.

**cricket**
There is one great similarity between music and cricket. There are slow movements in both.
NEVILLE CARDUS.

**customer**
The customer is always right.
H. GORDON SELFRIDGE.

**cynic**
A cynic is a man who knows the price of everything and the value of nothing.
OSCAR WILDE.

# D

**day**
It was such a lovely day I thought it was a pity to get up.
W. SOMERSET MAUGHAM.

**dead**

What I like about Clive
Is that he is no longer alive.
There is a great deal to be said
For being dead.

E.C. BENTLEY.

**death**

I'm not afraid to die; I just don't want
to be there when it happens.

WOODY ALLEN.

After the first death, there is no other.

DYLAN THOMAS.

I have lost friends, some by death,
others through sheer inability to cross
the street.

VIRGINIA WOOLF.

**devil**

It is stupid of modern civilization to
have given up believing in the devil
when he is the only explanation of it.

RONALD KNOX.

**diary**

Keep a diary and one day it will keep
you.

MAE WEST.

**die**

To die will be an awfully big adventure.

J.M. BARRIE.

Die, my dear doctor? That's the last
thing I shall do.

LORD PALMERSTON.

**directions**

Lord Ronald ... flung himself upon his
horse and rode madly off in all
directions.

STEPHEN LEACOCK.

**discretion** Discretion is the better part of
valour. WILLIAM SHAKESPEARE. The
correct quotation is: 'The better part of
valour is discretion.'.

**disgruntled**

I could see that, if not actually
disgruntled, he was far from being
gruntled.

P.G. WODEHOUSE.

**dog**

A dog is the only thing on earth that
loves you more than you love yourself.

JOSH BILLINGS.

Any man who hates dogs and babies
can't be all bad.

LEO C. ROSTEN.

The noblest of all dogs is the hot dog; it
feeds the hand that bites it.

LAURENCE J. PETER.

**dontopedalogy**

Dontopedalogy is the science of
opening your mouth and putting your
foot in it.

PRINCE PHILIP (DUKE OF EDINBURGH.)

**down and out**

When you are down and out something
always turns up – and it is usually the
noses of your friends.

ORSON WELLES.

THE NOBLEST OF ALL DOGS IS THE HOT DOG.
IT FEEDS THE HAND THAT BITES IT.

9

**dreams**

But I, being poor, have only my
dreams;
I have spread my dreams under your
feet;
Tread softly because you tread on my
dreams.

W.B. YEATS.

**drowning**

I was much too far out all my life,
And not waving but drowning.

STEVIE SMITH.

**dull**

There are no dull subjects. There are
only dull writers.

H.L. MENCKEN.

**dying**

Dying is a very dull, dreary affair. My
advice to you is to have nothing
whatever to do with it.

W. SOMERSET MAUGHAM.

Dying
Is an art, like everything else.
I do it exceptionally well.

SYLVIA PLATH.

# E

**ears**

His ears make him look like a taxi with
both doors open.

HOWARD HUGHES (referring to
Clark Gable).

It's all very well to be able to write
books, but can you waggle your ears?

J.M. BARRIE.

**earth**

The meek shall inherit the earth, but
not its mineral rights.

J. PAUL GETTY.

**earthquake**

What we want is a story that starts with
an earthquake and works its way up to
a climax.

SAM GOLDWYN.

**east**

Oh, East is East, and West is West, and
never the twain shall meet.

RUDYARD KIPLING.

**education**

Education has for its object the
formation of character.

HERBERT SPENCER.

Education is what survives when what
has been learned has been forgotten.

B.F. SKINNER.

**elephant**
I have a memory like an elephant. In fact, elephants often consult me.

NOËL COWARD.

**enemies**
Do not fear when your enemies criticize you. Beware when they applaud.

VO DONG GIANG.

**England**
That there's some corner of a foreign
  field
That is for ever England.

RUPERT BROOKE.

Oh, to be in England
Now that April's there.

ROBERT BROWNING.

**English**
This is the sort of English up with which I will not put.

WINSTON CHURCHILL.

An Englishman, even if he is alone, forms an orderly queue of one.

GEORGE MIKES.

An Englishman thinks he is moral only when he is uncomfortable.

GEORGE BERNARD SHAW.

**enjoy**
The only way to enjoy anything in this life is to earn it first.

GINGER ROGERS.

**equal**
All animals are equal, but some animals are more equal than others.

GEORGE ORWELL.

All men are born equal, but quite a few eventually get over it.

LORD MANCROFT.

**evolution**
Evolution is far more important than living.

ERNST JUNGER.

**excuses**
Several excuses are always less convincing than one.

ALDOUS HUXLEY.

**facts**
The trouble with facts is that there are so many of them.

SAMUEL MCCHORD CROTHERS.

Generally, the theories we believe we call facts and the facts we disbelieve we call theories.

FELIX COHEN.

**failure**
There is much to be said for failure. It is more interesting than success.

MAX BEERBOHM.

There is no formula for success. But there is a formula for failure, and that is trying to please everybody.

NICHOLAS RAY.

**fairies**
There are fairies at the bottom of our garden!

ROSE FYLEMAN.

**famous**
It took me fifteen years to discover I had no talent for writing, but I couldn't give it up, because by that time I was too famous.

ROBERT BENCHLEY.

The tragedy of being famous is that you have to devote so much time to being famous.

PABLO PICASSO.

**fancy**
A little of what you fancy does you good.

MARIE LLOYD. 11

**fat**

Imprisoned in every fat man a thin one is wildly signalling to be let out.

CYRIL CONNOLLY.

**fate**

I am the master of my fate;
I am the captain of my soul.

W.E. HENLEY.

Fate keeps on happening.

ANITA LOOS.

**father**

And when did you last see your father?

W.F. YEAMES.

**fear**

The only thing we have to fear is fear itself.

FRANKLIN D. ROOSEVELT.

We fear something before we hate it. A child who fears noises becomes a man who hates noises.

CYRIL CONNOLLY.

Fear is essential. It is like a drug.

LUIS MIGUEL DOMINGUIN.

**female**

For the female of the species is more deadly than the male.

RUDYARD KIPLING.

**fence**

If the fence is strong enough I'll sit on it.

CYRIL SMITH.

**few**

Never in the field of human conflict was so much owed by so many to so few.

WINSTON CHURCHILL (*1940*).

**fight**

We shall fight on the beaches, we shall fight on the landing grounds, we shall fight in the fields and in the streets, we shall fight in the hills; we shall never surrender.

WINSTON CHURCHILL (*1940*).

**film**

Every film should have a beginning, a middle and an end – but not necessarily in that order.

JEAN-LUC GODARD.

A film is never really good unless the camera is an eye in the head of a poet.

ORSON WELLES.

**firm**

I am firm. You are obstinate. He is a pig-headed fool.

KATHARINE WHITEHORN.

**fisherman**

All you need to be a fisherman is patience and a worm.

HERB SHRINER.

**flowers**

Where have all the flowers gone?
The young girls picked them every one.

PETE SEEGER.

### folk-singer
A folk-singer is someone who sings through his nose by ear.

ANON.

### food
On the Continent, people have good food; in England people have good table manners.

GEORGE MIKES

### football
Some people think football is a matter of life and death. . . . I can assure you it is much more serious than that.

BILL SHANKLY.

### friend
A friend in need is a friend to be avoided.

LORD SAMUEL.

I do not believe that friends are necessarily the people you like best, they are merely the people who got there first.

PETER USTINOV.

### funny
What do you mean, funny? Funny peculiar or funny ha-ha?

IAN HAY.

### future
I have seen the future, and it works.

LINCOLN STEFFENS.

I never think of the future. It comes soon enough.

ALBERT EINSTEIN.

The best thing about the future is that it only comes one day at a time.

DEAN ACHESON.

### gamesmanship
Or the Art of Winning Games without Actually Cheating.

STEPHEN POTTER.

### genius
The genius of Einstein leads to Hiroshima.

PABLO PICASSO.

Genius is one per cent inspiration and ninety-nine per cent perspiration.

THOMAS A. EDISON.

13

THE UNSPEAKABLE IN FULL PURSUIT OF THE UNEATABLE

**gentleman**
The English country gentleman galloping after a fox – the unspeakable in full pursuit of the uneatable.

OSCAR WILDE.

**gluttony**
"What I like about gluttony," a bishop I once knew used to say, "is that it doesn't hurt anyone else.".

MONICA FURLONG.

**goal**
You've got a goal. I've got a goal. Now all we need is a football team.

GROUCHO MARX.

**golf**
Golf is a game whose aim is to hit a very small ball into an even smaller hole, with weapons singularly ill-designed for the purpose.

WINSTON CHURCHILL.

**good**
On the whole human beings want to be good, but not too good, and not quite all the time.

GEORGE ORWELL.

**goodness**
Goodness is easier to recognize than to define.

W.H. AUDEN.

**gourmet**
A gourmet is just a glutton with brains.

PHILIP W. HABERMAN JR.

**greatest**
I am the greatest.

MUHAMMAD ALI.

**grown-ups**
One of the most obvious facts about grown-ups to a child is that they have forgotten what it is like to be a child.

RANDALL JARRELL.

**guest**
The art of being a good guest is to know when to leave.

PRINCE PHILIP (DUKE OF EDINBURGH).

**guilty**
It is better that ten guilty persons escape than one innocent suffer.

SIR WILLIAM BLACKSTONE.

**haircut**
Don't ask the barber whether you need a haircut.

DANIEL S. GREENBERG.

**happiness**
One should never let one's happiness depend on other people.

H. GRANVILLE BARKER.

Only in romantic novels are the beautiful guaranteed happiness.

LADY CYNTHIA ASQUITH.

There is no such thing as the pursuit of happiness, but there is the discovery of joy.

JOYCE GRENFELL.

**happy**
Even if we can't be happy, we must always be cheerful.

IRVING KRISTOL.

**hatchet**
No one ever forgets where he buried the hatchet.

KIM HUBBARD.

**health**
Too much health is unhealthy.

LEO C. ROSTEN.

**healthy**
Early to rise and early to bed
Makes a male healthy, wealthy and dead.

JAMES THURBER.

**heaven**
If you go to Heaven without being naturally qualified for it, you will not enjoy yourself there.

GEORGE BERNARD SHAW.

**hell**
In hell there is no other punishment than to begin over and over again the tasks left unfinished in your lifetime.

ANDRÉ GIDE.

**heroes**
People are only heroes when they cannot do anything else.

PAUL CLAUDEL.

**hesitates**
He who hesitates is sometimes saved.

JAMES THURBER.

**historian**
The novelist is the historian of the present. The historian is the novelist of the past.

GEORGES DUHAMEL.

**history**
History, Stephen said, is a nightmare from which I am trying to awake.

JAMES JOYCE.

History is an endless repetition of the wrong way of living.

LAWRENCE DURRELL.

History teaches us that men and nations behave wisely once they have exhausted all other alternatives.

ABBA EBAN.

The history of the world is the record of a man in quest of his daily bread and butter.

H.W. VAN LOON.

**Hitler**
Hitler was a profoundly *uneducated* man of genius; there could be nothing more dangerous ...

A.L. ROWSE.

**hole**
A hole is nothing at all, but you can break your neck on it.

AUSTIN O'MALLEY. 15

**holidays**
Term, holidays, term, holidays, till we leave school, and then work, work, work till we die.

C.S. LEWIS.

**Hollywood**
Hollywood – a place where the inmates are in charge of the asylum.

LAURENCE STALLINGS.

**home**
Too many young people are beginning to regard home as a filling station by day and a parking place for the night.

REV. WILLIAM JOYCE.

**hope**
A poet's hope: to be, like some valley cheese, local, but prized elsewhere.

W.H. AUDEN.

AN INGENIOUS ASSEMBLY OF PORTABLE PLUMBING.

**horse**
A horse is dangerous at both ends and uncomfortable in the middle.

IAN FLEMING.

**host**
The happy host makes a sad guest.

HAROLD ACTON.

**house**
A house is a machine for living in.

LE CORBUSIER.

**human**
A human being: an ingenious assembly of portable plumbing.

CHRISTOPHER MORLEY.

The human species is, to some extent, the result of mistakes which arrested our development and prevented us from assuming the somewhat unglamorous form of our primitive ancestors.

JONATHAN MILLER.

**humour**
Humour is practically the only thing about which the English are utterly serious.

MALCOLM MUGGERIDGE.

I have a fine sense of the ridiculous, but no sense of humour.

EDWARD ALBEE.

**ill**
One of the minor pleasures of life is to be slightly ill.

HAROLD NICOLSON.

**influence**
How to win friends and influence people.

DALE CARNEGIE.

# J

# K

**jazz**
What they call jazz is just the music of people's emotions.
WILLIE 'THE LION' SMITH.

**joke**
A joke isn't a joke until someone laughs.
MICHAEL CRAWFORD.

**journalists**
Journalists say a thing they know isn't true, in the hope that if they keep on saying it long enough it *will* be true.
ARNOLD BENNETT.

**justice**
Justice should not only be done, but should manifestly and undoubtedly be seen to be done.
LORD HEWART.

**kids**
There are three ways to get something done; do it yourself, hire someone, or forbid your kids to do it.
MONTA CRANE.

**killed**
Was it you or your brother who was killed in the war?
REV. WILLIAM SPOONER.

**kills**
Wild animals never kill for sport. Man is the only one to whom the torture and death of his fellow creatures is amusing in itself.
J.A. FROUDE.

**kleptomaniac**
A kleptomaniac is someone who helps himself because he can't help himself.
ANON. 17

**lamps**

The lamps are going out all over
Europe; we shall not see them lit again
in our lifetime.

VISCOUNT GREY OF FALLODON (*1914*).

**laugh**

Laugh, and the world laughs with you;
Weep, and you weep alone,
For the sad old earth must borrow its
  mirth,
But has trouble enough of its own.

ELLA WHEELER WILCOX.

**letting go**

It's all right letting yourself go, as long
as you can get yourself back.

MICK JAGGER.

**liberty**

Liberty is the right to tell people what
they do not want to hear.

GEORGE ORWELL.

**lie**

If one cannot invent a really convincing
lie, it is often better to stick to the truth.

ANGELA THIRKELL.

> **lie** A lie travels round the world while
> truth is putting on her boots. REV.
> C.H. SPURGEON. He was misquoted by
> James Callaghan, who said: "A lie can
> be halfway round the world before the
> truth has got its boots on.".

**light**

My candle burns at both ends;
It will not last the night;
But, ah, my foes, and oh my friends –
It gives a lovely light.

EDNA ST VINCENT MILLAY.

**literature**

Literature is the art of writing
something that will be read twice;
journalism what will be grasped at
once.

CYRIL CONNOLLY.

**life**

Life is a zoo in a jungle.

PETER DE VRIES.

**love**

Love is a many-splendoured thing.

HAN SUYIN.

The paths of love are rougher
Than thoroughfares of stones.

THOMAS HARDY.

Love conquers all things except poverty
and toothache.

MAE WEST.

**loved**

'Tis better to have loved and lost
Than never to have loved at all.

ALFRED, LORD TENNYSON.

**luck**

We must believe in luck. For how else
can we explain the success of those we
don't like?

JEAN COCTEAU.

**lunatic**

Every reform movement has a lunatic
fringe.

THEODORE ROOSEVELT.

**mad dogs**

Mad dogs and Englishmen go out in
the midday sun.

NOËL COWARD.

**man**

Man is a clever animal who behaves
like an imbecile.

ALBERT SCHWEITZER.

**mankind**

I love mankind; it's people I can't
stand.

CHARLES M. SCHULZ.

**manners**

The reason nobody talks in England is
because children are taught manners
instead of conversation.

ROBERT MORLEY.

**mathematics**

Mathematics . . . possesses not only
truth, but supreme beauty – a beauty
cold and austere, like that of sculpture.

BERTRAND RUSSELL.

**memory**

Memory is more indelible than ink.

ANITA LOOS.

**men**

Men are like wine – some turn to
vinegar, but the best improve with age.

POPE JOHN XXIII.

Some of my best leading men have been
dogs and horses.

ELIZABETH TAYLOR.

**mind**

The human mind is like an umbrella. It
functions best when open.

WALTER GROPIUS.

THE HUMAN MIND
IS LIKE AN UMBRELLA.
IT FUNCTIONS BEST
WHEN OPEN.

## money

Money isn't everything: usually it isn't even enough.

ANON.

I don't care too much for money,
Money can't buy me love.

JOHN LENNON AND
PAUL McCARTNEY.

> **money** Money is the root of all evil.
> THE BIBLE, *Timothy, 6:10*. actually reads:
> 'The love of money is the root of all
> evil.'.

## mother

Nobody can misunderstand a boy like his own mother.

NORMAN DOUGLAS.

## music

All music is singing. The ideal is to make the orchestra play like singers.

BRUNO WALTER.

I don't know anything about music. In my line you don't have to.

ELVIS PRESLEY.

I hate music, especially when it's played.

JIMMY DURANTE.

Popular music is popular because a lot of people like it.

IRVING BERLIN.

## my way

I did it my way.

PAUL ANKA.

## needs

One of the weaknesses of our age is our apparent inability to distinguish our needs from our greeds.

DON ROBINSON.

## nothing

Nothing matters very much and few things matter at all.

LORD BALFOUR.

One of the lessons of history is that nothing is often a good thing to do and always a clever thing to say.

WILL DURANT.

## novel

This is not a novel to be tossed aside lightly. It should be thrown with great force.

DOROTHY PARKER.

## number

Well, if I called the wrong number, why did you answer the phone?

JAMES THURBER.

## old

Anyone can get old. All you have to do is live long enough.

GROUCHO MARX.

They shall grow not old, as we that are left grow old.

LAURENCE BINYON.

Growing old is something you do if you're lucky.

GROUCHO MARX.

It's sad to grow old, but nice to ripen.

BRIGITTE BARDOT.

No man is ever old enough to know better.

HOLBROOK JACKSON.

## old age

Old age is always 15 years older than I am.

BERNARD BARUCH.

I prefer old age to the alternative.

MAURICE CHEVALIER.

**opera**
Nobody really sings in an opera. They just make loud noises.

AMELITA GALLI-CURCI.

**optimist**
The optimist proclaims that we live in the best of all possible worlds; and the pessimist fears this is true.

JAMES BRANCH CABELL.

**overtakers**
It's the overtakers who keep the undertakers busy.

WILLIAM PITTS.

**pains**
I can sympathize with people's pains, but not with their pleasures.

ALDOUS HUXLEY.

**paradises**
The true paradises are the paradises we have lost.

MARCEL PROUST.

**parliament**
There are three golden rules for Parliamentary speakers: 'Stand up. Speak up. Shut up.'

J.W. LOWTHER.

**past**
It's a waste of time thinking hard about the past. There's nothing you can do to change it.

ERTÉ (ROMAIN DE TIRTOFF).

The great thing about the past is that it's happened.

FRANK NORMAN.

The past is a foreign country: they do things differently there.

L.P. HARTLEY.

**patience**
Patience is not only a virtue. It pays.

B.C. FORBES.

**patient**
I am extraordinarily patient, provided I get my own way in the end.

MARGARET THATCHER.

**pauses**
The most precious things in speech are the pauses.

RALPH RICHARDSON.

**people**
People don't change, they only become more so.

JOHN BRIGHT-HOLMES.

The world is divided into people who do things – and people who get the credit.

DWIGHT MORROW.

Believe me, of all the people in the world, those who want the most are those who have the most.

DAVID GRAYSON.

**performance**
The only thing you owe to the public is a good performance.

HUMPHREY BOGART.

**pessimist**
A pessimist is a man who looks both ways when he's crossing a one-way street.

LAURENCE J. PETER.

**Philadelphia** On the whole, I'd rather be in Philadelphia. W.C. FIELDS. His actual words were "Here lies W.C. Fields. I would rather be living in Philadelphia.". He suggested that this should be engraved on his gravestone but this was not done.

21

**play**
Play it, Sam.

HUMPHREY BOGART (*in the film* Casablanca).

---

**play** "Play it again, Sam." HUMPHREY BOGART, in the film *Casablanca*. In fact, there are two quotations, neither as printed above. The first line was spoken by Ingrid Bergman, who said: "Play it, Sam. Play *As Time Goes By*.". The second line was spoken by Humphrey Bogart, who said: "If she can stand it, I can. Play it.".

---

**poet**
A poet is, before anything else, a person who is passionately in love with language.

W.H. AUDEN.

**poetry**
There's no money in poetry; but then there's no poetry in money either.

ROBERT GRAVES.

Poetry is the supreme fiction, madame.

WALLACE STEVENS.

**politician**
A politician is an animal that can sit on a fence and keep both ears to the ground.

H.L. MENCKEN.

The only way a reporter should look at a politician is down.

FRANK KENT.

**politics**
Politics is the art of the possible.

R.A. BUTLER.

**pope**
Anybody can be Pope; the proof of this is that I have become one.

POPE JOHN XXIII.

**portraits**
You don't change the course of history by turning the faces of portraits to the wall.

JAWAHARLAL NEHRU.

**poverty**
I worked my way up from nothing to a state of extreme poverty.

GROUCHO MARX.

Poverty is no disgrace to a man, but it is confoundedly inconvenient.

SYDNEY SMITH.

**power**
Power tends to corrupt, and absolute power corrupts absolutely.

LORD ACTON.

All power is delightful, and absolute power is absolutely delightful.

KENNETH TYNAN.

**prayers**
Hush! Hush! Whisper who dares! Christopher Robin is saying his prayers.

A.A.MILNE.

**president**
Anyone who wants to be President should have his head examined.

AVERELL HARRIMAN.

**prison**
It's not the people in prison who worry me. It's the people who aren't.

EARL OF ARRAN.

**prisoner**
A prisoner of war is a man who tries to kill you and fails, and then asks you not to kill him.

WINSTON CHURCHILL.

**professor**
A professor is someone who talks in someone else's sleep.

W.H. AUDEN.

**progress**
Progress was all right. Only it went on too long.

JAMES THURBER.

**qualities**
It is not for our faults that we are disliked and even hated, but for our qualities.

BERNARD BERENSON.

**quote**
I often quote myself. It adds spice to my conversation.

GEORGE BERNARD SHAW.

**race**
It is not possible to regard our race with anything but alarm. From primeval ooze to the stars, we killed anything that stood in our way, including each other.

GORE VIDAL.

**radio**
Radio is a creative theatre of the mind.

WOLFMAN JACK SMITH.

**rainbow**
Somewhere over the rainbow,
Way up high:
There's a land that I heard of
Once in a lullaby.

E.Y. HARBURG.  23

**rat**
The trouble with the rat race is that even if you win, you're still a rat.

LILY TOMLIN.

**reality**
Human kind
Cannot bear very much reality.

T.S. ELIOT.

The dignity of man lies in his ability to face reality in all its meaninglessness.

MARTIN ESSLIN.

**religion**
There is only one religion, though there are a hundred versions of it.

GEORGE BERNARD SHAW.

**remember**
Those who cannot remember the past are condemned to repeat it.

GEORGE SANTAYANA.

**rich**
I have been poor and I have been rich. Rich is better.

SOPHIE TUCKER.

**right**
Doing what's right isn't the problem. It's knowing what's right.

LYNDON B. JOHNSON.

**room**
All I want is a room somewhere,
Far away from the cold night air.

ALAN JAY LERNER.

**rumours**
I hate to spread rumours; but what else can one do with them?

AMANDA LEAR.

# S

**scenery**
The scenery was beautiful, but the actors got in front of it.

ALEXANDER WOOLLCOTT.

**school**
No one who had any sense ever liked school.

LORD BOOTHBY.

**Shakespeare**
I know not, sir, whether Bacon wrote the words of Shakespeare, but if he did not, it seems to me he missed the opportunity of his life.

J.M. BARRIE.

**ship**
All I ask is a tall ship and a star to steer her by.

JOHN MASEFIELD.

**show business**
There's no business like show business.

IRVING BERLIN.

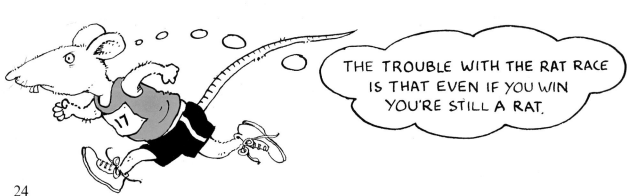

THE TROUBLE WITH THE RAT RACE IS THAT EVEN IF YOU WIN YOU'RE STILL A RAT.

**Shredded Wheat**
He dreamed he was eating Shredded Wheat and woke up to find the mattress half gone.

FRED ALLEN.

**sick**
A youth with his first cigar makes himself sick; a youth with his first girl makes other people sick.

MARY WILSON LITTLE.

**sitting**
Are you sitting comfortably? Then I'll begin.

JULIA LANG.

**sixty-four**
Will you still need me, will you still feed me,
When I'm sixty-four?

JOHN LENNON AND
PAUL McCARTNEY.

**small**
Small is beautiful.

E.F. SCHUMACHER.

**snore**
Laugh and the world laughs with you; snore and you sleep alone.

ANTHONY BURGESS.

**space**
Space isn't remote at all. It's only an hour's drive away if your car could go straight upwards.

SIR FRED HOYLE.

**speech**
It usually takes me more than three weeks to prepare a good impromptu speech.

MARK TWAIN.

**sponge**
If I believed in reincarnation, I'd come back as a sponge.

WOODY ALLEN.

**stare**
What is this life, if full of care,
We have no time to stand and stare?

W.H. DAVIES.

SPACE ISN'T REMOTE AT ALL. IT'S ONLY AN HOUR'S DRIVE AWAY IF YOUR CAR COULD GO STRAIGHT UPWARD.

25

**stars**

Two men look out through the same
  bars:
One sees the mud, and one the stars.

FREDERICK LANGBRIDGE.

**statesman**

A statesman is a politician who's been
dead for ten or fifteen years.

HARRY S. TRUMAN.

When you're abroad, you're a
statesman; when you're at home, you're
just a politician.

HAROLD MACMILLAN.

**step**

That's one small step for a man, one
giant leap for mankind.

NEIL A. ARMSTRONG (*The first Moon
                     landing, 1969*)

**story-teller**

A good story-teller is a person who has
a good memory and hopes the others
haven't.

IRWIN S. COBB.

**striving**

Year by year we are becoming better
equipped to accomplish the things we
are striving for. But what are we
actually striving for?

BERTRAND DE JOUVENAL.

**stupidity**

Stupidity is mainly just a lack of
capacity to take things in.

CLIVE JAMES.

**style**

Style is knowing who you are, what you
want to say, and not giving a damn.

GORE VIDAL.

**succeed**

It is not enough to succeed. Others
must fail.

GORE VIDAL.

A STATESMAN IS A POLITICIAN WHO'S BEEN DEAD FOR 10 OR 15 YEARS

**success**

The common idea that success spoils
people by making them vain, egotistic
and self-complacent is erroneous – on
the contrary it makes them, for the
most part, humble, tolerant and kind.
Failure makes people bitter and cruel.

W. SOMERSET MAUGHAM.

The toughest thing about success is that
you've got to keep on being a success.

IRVING BERLIN.

**survival**

Survival of the fittest.

HERBERT SPENCER.

**tact**

Tact consists in knowing how to go too
far.

JEAN COCTEAU.

**talent**

Talent is the least important thing a performer needs, but humility is the one thing he must have.

CLARK GABLE.

**taxidermist**

A tall, drooping man, looking as if he had been stuffed in a hurry by an incompetent taxidermist.

P.G. WODEHOUSE.

**tears**

I have nothing to offer but blood, toil, tears and sweat.

WINSTON CHURCHILL (*1940*).

**television**

Television is an invention that permits you to be entertained in your own living-room by people you wouldn't have in your home.

DAVID FROST.

Television is for appearing on, not looking at.

NOËL COWARD.

TV is an evil medium. It should never have been invented, but since we have to live with it, let us try to do something about it.

RICHARD BURTON.

Why should people pay good money to go out and see bad films when they can stay at home and see bad television for nothing?

SAM GOLDWYN.

**temptation**

I can resist everything except temptation.

OSCAR WILDE.

The last temptation is the greatest treason:
To do the right deed for the wrong reason.

T.S. ELIOT.

**things**

It was great fun,
But it was just one of those things.

COLE PORTER.

**time**

Time goes, you say? Ah no!
Alas, Time stays, *we* go.

AUSTIN DOBSON.

Time present and time past
Are both perhaps present in time future
And time future contained in time past.

T.S.ELIOT.

Modern man thinks he loves something – time – when he does not do things quickly. Yet he does not know what to do with the time he gains – except kill it.

ERICH FROMM.

So little time, so little to do.

OSCAR LEVANT. 27

**tongue**
Fighting is essentially a masculine idea;
a woman's weapon is her tongue.
HERMIONE GINGOLD.

**tools**
Give us the tools and we'll finish the job.
WINSTON CHURCHILL.

**toothpaste**
Once the toothpaste is out of the tube,
it's hard to get it back in.
H.R. HALDEMAN.

**tragedy**
It is the tragedy of the world that no-
one knows what he doesn't know; and
the less a man knows, the more sure he
is that he knows everything.
JOYCE CARY.

**train**
The only way of catching a train I ever
discovered is to miss the train before.
G.K. CHESTERTON.

**tree**
I think that I shall never see
A poem lovely as a tree.
JOYCE KILMER.

**troubles**
Pack up your troubles in your old kit-
bag.
GEORGE ASAF.

**truth**
In seeking truth you have to get both
sides of a story.
WALTER CRONKITE.
It has always been desirable to tell the
truth, but seldom, if ever, necessary.
A.J. BALFOUR.
The first casualty when war comes is
truth.
HIRAM JOHNSON.
The truth is rarely pure, and never
simple.
OSCAR WILDE.

Truth is a rare and precious
    commodity.
We must be sparing in its use.
C.P. SCOTT.
Truth may be stranger than fiction, but
fiction is truer.
FREDERIC RAPHAEL.

**uncertainty**
A little uncertainty is good for
everyone.
HENRY KISSINGER.

**unhappiness**
Unhappiness is defined as the difference
between our talents and our
expectations.
EDWARD DE BONO.

**unhappy**
All happy families resemble one
another, but each unhappy family is
unhappy in its own way.
LEO TOLSTOY.

**value**
What you really value is what you miss,
not what you have.
JORGE LUIS BORGES.

**Venice**
Venice is like eating an entire box of
chocolate liqueurs at one go.
TRUMAN CAPOTE.

**violence**
Violence is the repartee of the illiterate.
ALAN BRIEN.

## walks
I like long walks, especially when they are taken by people who annoy me.

FRED ALLEN.

## waltzing
And he sang as he sat and waited for
  his billy-boil,
'You'll come a-waltzing, Matilda, with
  me.'

A.B. PATERSON.

## wanting
As soon as you stop wanting something, you get it.

ANDY WARHOL

## war
It is better to win the peace and to lose the war.

BOB MARLEY.

In war, you don't have to be nice, you only have to be right.

WINSTON CHURCHILL.

Mankind must put an end to war or war will put an end to mankind.

JOHN F. KENNEDY.

The quickest way of ending a war is to lose it.

GEORGE ORWELL.

War is fear cloaked in courage.

GENERAL WILLIAM WESTMORELAND.

## water
You can analyse a glass of water and you're left with a lot of chemical components, but nothing you can drink.

J.B.S. HALDANE.

## west
Go West, young man, Go West!

J.L.B. SOULE.

## whimper
This is the way the world ends
Not with a bang but a whimper.

T.S. ELIOT.

## wind
The wind of change is blowing through the continent.

HAROLD MACMILLAN.

## winter
Now is the winter of our discontent made glorious summer by central heating.

JACK SHARKEY.

A cold coming we had of it,
Just the worst time of the year
For a journey, and such a long journey:
The ways deep and the weather sharp,
The very dead of winter.

T.S. ELIOT.

## wisdom
Wisdom is knowing when you can't be wise

PAUL ENGLE.

## women
I hate women because they always know where things are.

JAMES THURBER.

There are no ugly women, only lazy ones.

HELENA RUBINSTEIN.

Whatever women do they must do twice as well as men to be thought half as good.

CHARLOTTE WHITTON.

Women are really much nicer than men. No wonder we like them.

KINGSLEY AMIS.

## wood
People love chopping wood. In this activity one immediately sees results.

ALBERT EINSTEIN. 29

**woodshed**

Something nasty in the woodshed.

STELLA GIBBONS.

**work**

I never forget that work is a curse –
which is why I've never made it a habit.

BLAISE CENDRARS.

Work expands so as to fill the time
available for its completion.

C. NORTHCOTE PARKINSON.

**workers**

The workers have nothing to lose but
their chains. They have a world to gain.
Workers of the world unite!

KARL MARX.

**world**

You have to have some order in a
disordered world.

FRANK LLOYD WRIGHT.

**Wren, Sir Christopher**

Sir Christopher Wren
Said 'I am going to dine with some
    men.
If anyone calls
Say I'm designing St Paul's.'

E.C. BENTLEY.

**writer**

It is by sitting down to write every
morning that one becomes a writer.
Those who do not do this remain
amateurs.

GERALD BRENAN.

If a writer disbelieves what he is
writing, then he can hardly expect his
reader to believe it.

JORGE LUIS BORGES.

**writers**

Writers should be read; but neither seen
nor heard.

DAPHNE DU MAURIER.

**wrong**

Two wrongs don't make a right, but
they make a good excuse.

THOMAS SZASZ.

30

If you want to know who any of the people quoted in this book are, you can look them up in the following, alphabetically-arranged list.

Dean Acheson, politician (1893–1971)
Sir Harold Acton, man of letters (1904– )
Lord Acton (Sir J.E.E. Dalberg), historian (1834–1902)
Edward Albee, playwright (1928– )
Fred Allen, comedian (1894–1956)
Woody Allen, actor (1935– )
Muhammad Ali, boxer (1942– )
Kingsley Amis, author (1922– )
Paul Anka, singer (1941– )
Neil A. Armstrong, astronaut (1930– )
Earl of Arran, journalist (1910–1983)
George Asaf, songwriter (1880–1951)
Lady Cynthia Asquith, hostess (1887–1960)
W.H. Auden, poet (1907–1973)
A.J. Balfour, politician (1848–1930)
Brigitte Bardot, film actress (1934– )
J.M.Barrie, playwright (1860–1937)
Bernard Baruch, financier (1870–1965)
Sir Edward Beddington-Behrens, lawyer & statesman
  (1897–1968)
Sir Thomas Beecham, conductor (1879–1961)
Max Beerbohm, author (1872–1956)
Hilaire Belloc, author (1870–1953)
Robert Benchley, humorist (1889–1945)
Arnold Bennett, author (1867–1931)
E.C. Bentley, writer (1875–1956)
Bernard Berenson, art historian (1865–1959)
Irving Berlin, songwriter (1888–1989)
Ugo Betti, playwright (1892–1953)
Ambrose Bierce, author (1842–1914)
Josh Billings, humorist (1818–1885)
Laurence Binyon, poet (1869–1943)
Sir William Blackstone, lawyer (1723–1780)
Col. Blashford-Snell, soldier (1936– )
Humphrey Bogart, film actor (1899–1957)
Lord Boothby, politician (1900–1986)
Jorge Luis Borges, writer (1899–1986)
Gerald Brenan, writer (1894–1987)
Alan Brien, writer (1925– )
John Bright-Holmes, publisher, (current)
Rupert Brooke, poet (1887–1915)
Robert Browning, poet(1812–1889)
Luis Buñuel, film director (1900–1983)
Anthony Burgess, author (1917– )
Richard Burton, actor (1925–1984)
R.A. Butler, statesman (1902–1982)
James Branch Cabell, novelist (1879–1958)
James Callaghan, statesman (1912– )
Truman Capote, author (1924–1984)
Al Capp, cartoonist (1909–1979)
Neville Cardus, writer (1889–1975)
Dale Carnegie, writer (1888–1955)
Lewis Carroll, writer (1832–1898)
Joyce Cary, British novelist (1888–1957)
Blaise Cendrars, novelist (1887–1961)
Charlie Chaplin, film actor & producer (1889–1977)
G.K. Chesterton, author (1874–1936)
Maurice Chevalier, actor & singer (1888–1972)
Agatha Christie, author (1891–1976)
Winston Churchill, statesman (1874–1965)
Paul Claudel, composer (1868–1955)
Irwin S. Cobb, author (1876–1944)
Jean Cocteau, writer & film director (1889–1963)
Cyril Connolly, writer (1903–1974)
Gary Cooper, film actor (1901–1961)
Noël Coward, actor, composer & director (1898–1973)
Michael Crawford, actor (1942– )
Walter Cronkite, newspaper columnist (1916– )
W.H. Davies, poet (1871–1940)

Edward de Bono, lecturer in medicine (1933– )
Charles de Gaulle, statesman (1890–1970)
Peter de Vries, writer (1910– )
Austin Dobson, poet (1840–1921)
Luis Miguel Dominguin, Spanish bullfighter
Norman Douglas, author (1886–1952)
Georges Duhamel, writer (1884–1966)
Daphne du Maurier, novelist (1907–1989)
Will Durant, historian (1885–1981)
Jimmy Durante, comedian (1893–1980)
Lawrence Durrell, author (1912–1990)
Abba Eban, statesman (1915– )
Thomas A. Edison, inventor (1847–1931)
Paul Ehrlich, scientist (1932– )
Albert Einstein, mathematician (1879–1955)
T.S. Eliot, poet & author (1888–1965)
Paul Engle, poet (1908– )
Erté (Romain de Tirtoff), designer (1892–1990)
Martin Esslin, writer (1918– )
W.C. Fields, actor & comedian (1880–1946)
Robert Fitzsimmons, boxer (1862–1917)
Ian Fleming, novelist (1908–1964)
Henry Fonda, actor (1905–1982)
B.C. Forbes, publisher (1880–1954)
Anatole France, author (1844–1924)
Erich Fromm, psychologist (1900–1980)
David Frost, TV presenter (1939– )
J.A. Froude (1818–1894)
Monica Furlong, novelist (1930– )
Rose Fyleman, writer (1877–1957)
Clark Gable, film actor (1901–1961)
Amelita Galli-Curci, singer (1889–1963)
J. Paul Getty, financier (1892–1976)
Stella Gibbons, novelist (1902–1989)
Andre Gide, writer (1869–1951)
W.S. Gilbert, playwright (1836–1911)
Hermione Gingold, actress (1897–1987)
George Gissing, novelist (1857–1903)
Jean-Luc Godard, film director (1930– )
Sam Goldwyn, film producer (1882–1974)
H. Granville-Barker, actor-manager (1877–1946)
Robert Graves, poet & writer (1895–1986)
David Grayson, journalist & author (1870–1946)
Daniel S. Greenberg, science writer (1931– )
Joyce Grenfell, entertainer (1910–1980)
Viscount Grey of Fallodon, statesman (1884–1916)
Walter Gropius, architect (1883–1969)
Gene Hackman, film actor (1930– )
Lord Hailsham (Quintin Hogg), statesman (1907– )
J.B.S. Haldane, scientist (1892–1964)
H.R. Haldeman, US official (1926– )
Alex Hamilton, journalist (1917– )
Richard Hamilton, artist (1922– )
E.Y. Harburg, lyricist (1896–1981)
Sir Cedric Hardwicke, actor (1893–1964)
Thomas Hardy, novelist (1840–1928)
Averell Harriman, statesman (1891–1986)
L.P. Hartley, novelist (1895–1972)
Ian Hay, novelist (1876–1952)
Lillian Hellman, playwright (1907–1984)
W.E. Henley, poet & playwright (1849–1903)
Lord Hewart, judge (1870–1943)
Alfred Hitchcock, film director (1899–1980)
Billie Holliday, singer (1915–1959)
Bob Hope, comedian (1904– )
Lord Hore-Belisha, statesman (1893–1957)
Sir Fred Hoyle, astronomer (1915– )
Wilfred Hyde White, actor (1903–1991)
Aldous Huxley, novelist (1894–1963)

Holbrook Jackson, writer (1874–1978)
Mick Jagger, singer (1943– )
Clive James, TV presenter (1939– )
Randall Jarrell, critic (1914–1965)
Pope John XXIII (1881–1963)
Hiram Johnson, politician (1866–1945)
Lyndon B. Johnson, politician (1908–1973)
James Joyce, novelist (1882–1941)
Ernst Junger, writer (1895– )
Buster Keaton, comedian (1895–1966)
John F. Kennedy, statesman (1917–1963)
Frank Kent, journalist (1907–1978)
Joyce Kilmer, poet (1886–1918)
Martin Luther King, religious leader (1929–1968)
Rudyard Kipling, author (1865–1936)
Henry Kissinger, statesman (1923– )
Ronald Knox, priest & author (1888–1957)
Irving Kristol, academic (1920– )
Julia Lang, actress & broadcaster (1921– )
Frederick Langbridge, priest, poet & playwright
    (1849–1923)
Stephen Leacock, humorous writer (1869–1944)
Le Corbusier (Charles Edouard Jeanneret), French
    architect (1881–1965)
John Lennon, singer (1941–1980)
Alan Jay Lerner, playwright (1918–1986)
Oscar Levant, musician (1906–1972)
C.S. Lewis, novelist (1898–1963)
Marie Lloyd, comedienne (1870–1922)
Anita Loos, author (1893–1981)
J.W. Lowther, speaker of the House of Commons
    (1855–1949)
Paul McCartney, singer & composer (1942– )
Harold Macmillan, statesman (1894–1988)
Lord Mancroft, politician (1914– )
Bob Marley, singer (1945–1981)
Groucho Marx, comedian (1895–1977)
Karl Marx, political theorist (1818–1883)
John Masefield, poet & author (1878–1967)
W. Somerset Maugham, novelist (1874–1965)
Louis B. Mayer, film producer (1885–1957)
H.L. Mencken, journalist & author (1880–1956)
George Mikes, author (1912– )
Edna St Vincent Millay, American poet (1892–1950)
Jonathan Miller, doctor, writer & producer (1936– )
A.A. Milne, author (1882–1956)
Christopher Morley, playwright (1890–1957)
Robert Morley, actor (1908–1992)
Desmond Morris, author & naturalist (1928– )
Dwight Morrow, lawyer & diplomat (1873–1931)
Malcolm Muggeridge, journalist (1903–1990)
H.H. Munro – see 'Saki'
Jawaharlal Nehru, statesman (1889–1964)
Harold Nicolson, politician (1886–1968)
Denis Norden, writer & broadcaster (1922– )
Frank Norman, author (1930–1980)
Conor Cruise O'Brien, editor (1917– )
Laurence Olivier (Lord Olivier), actor (1907–1989)
Baroness Orczy, novelist (1865–1947)
George Orwell, novelist & essayist (1903–1950)
Lord Palmerston, statesman (1784–1865)
Dorothy Parker, writer (1893–1967)
C. Northcote Parkinson, writer (1909– )
Eric Partridge, lexicographer (1894–1979)
A.B. Paterson, writer (1864–1961)
Prince Philip (Duke of Edinburgh), (1921– )
Pablo Picasso, painter (1881–1973)
Sylvia Plath, poet (1932–1968)
Cole Porter, composer & lyricist (1891–1964)
Stephen Potter, writer (1900–1969)
Elvis Presley, singer (1935–1977)
Marcel Proust, novelist (1871–1922)
Frederic Raphael, novelist (1931– )
Nicholas Ray, film director (1911– )
Ralph Richardson, actor (1902–1983)

Ginger Rogers, film actress (1911– )
Franklin D. Roosevelt, statesman (1882–1945)
Theodore Roosevelt, statesman (1858–1919)
Leo C. Rosten, writer (1908– )
A.L. Rowse, academic (1903– )
Helena Rubinstein, beautician (1872–1965)
John Ruskin, poet & critic (1819–1900)
Bertrand Russell, philosopher (1872–1970)
'Saki' (H.H. Munro), novelist (1870–1916)
Lord Samuel, statesman (1870–1963)
George Santayana, philosopher (1863–1952)
Charles M. Schulz, cartoonist (1922– )
E.F. Schumacher, economist (1911–1977)
Albert Schweitzer, doctor & missionary (1875–1965)
C.P.Scott, journalist (1846–1932)
George C. Scott, film actor (1926– )
Pete Seeger, singer (1919– )
H. Gordon Selfridge, store owner (1864–1947)
Robert Service, poet (1874–1958)
Dr Theodor Seuss, writer (1904– )
Bill Shankly, soccer manager (1918–1981)
George Bernard Shaw, playwright (1856–1950)
B.F. Skinner, American psychiatrist (1904– )
Stevie Smith, poet (1902–1971)
Sydney Smith, clergyman & essayist (1771–1845)
Willie 'The Lion' Smith, jazz musician (1895–1973)
Wolfman Jack Smith, disc jockey
J.L.B. Soule, editor & author (1815–1891)
Herbert Spencer, philosopher (1820–1903)
Laurence Stallings, writer (1894–1968)
Lincoln Steffens, journalist (1866–1936)
John Steinbeck, novelist (1902–1968)
Wallace Stevens, poet (1879–1955)
Han Suyin, novelist (1917– )
Thomas Szasz, psychiatrist (1920– )
Elizabeth Taylor, film actress (1932– )
Lord Taylor of Gryfe, businessman (1912– )
Alfred, Lord Tennyson, poet (1809–1892)
Margaret Thatcher, stateswoman (1925– )
Angela Thirkell, author (1890–1961)
Dylan Thomas, poet (1914–1953)
James Thurber, humorist & cartoonist (1894–1961)
Leo Tolstoy, novelist (1828–1910)
Lily Tomlin, comedienne (1939– )
Harry S. Truman, statesman (1884–1972)
Sophie Tucker, entertainer (1884–1966)
Mark Twain, novelist (1835–1910)
Kenneth Tynan, critic (1927–1980)
Peter Ustinov, actor, author & playwright (1921– )
H.W. Van Loon, author (1882–1944)
Queen Victoria (1819–1901)
Gore Vidal, author (1925– )
Edgar Wallace, novelist (1875–1932)
Henry Wallace, politician (1888–1965)
Bruno Walter, musician (1876–1962)
Andy Warhol, artist & film-maker (1926–1988)
Orson Welles, actor & director (1915–1985)
H.G. Wells, novelist (1886–1946)
Mae West, film actress (1893–1980)
Gen. William Westmoreland, soldier (1914– )
James McNeill Whistler, artist (1834–1903)
Charlotte Whitton, writer (1896–1975)
Ella Wheeler Wilcox, poet (1850–1919)
Oscar Wilde, playwright (1854–1900)
Harry Williams, songwriter (1874–1924)
P.G. Wodehouse, novelist & lyricist (1881–1975)
Tom Wolfe, writer (1931– )
Virginia Woolf, novelist (1882–1941)
Alexander Woollcott, critic (1887–1943)
Frank Lloyd Wright, architect (1869–1959)
W.F. Yeames, painter (1835–1918)
W.B. Yeats, poet (1865–1939)
Israel Zangwill, playwright & novelist (1864–1926)
Adolph Zukor, film producer (1873–1976)